The Official G

ENGLISH

GLOBAL GEOPARK

400 million years in the making...

English Riviera

GLOBAL GEOPARK

Foreword by **Professor Iain Stewart**

Illustration by Bex Glover
WWW.SEVERNSTUDIOS.CO.UK © 2010

Written by: Melanie Border, English Riviera Global Geopark Coordinator, Dr Chris Proctor and John Risdon
Compiled by: Melanie Border and Georgina Bowen, English Riviera Tourist Board
Editor: Alison Moss
Design: Dan Sutterby
Publishing Manager: Susan Sutterby (susan@coastalpublishing.co.uk)

First published in 2010 by Coastal Publishing, The Studio, Puddletown Road, Wareham, Dorset BH20 6AE
T: 01929 552233 E: enquiries@coastalpublishing.co.uk www.coastalpublishing.co.uk
Coastal Publishing is a Sillson Communications Ltd Company © Coastal Publishing 2010 all rights reserved

ISBN 978-0-9544845-8-3

British Library Cataloguing-in-Publication Data. A catalogue record for this book is available from the British Library.

The sale of this book helps support conservation and education programmes in the English Riviera Global Geopark
www.englishrivierageopark.org.uk

Printed and bound in the UK

Image acknowledgements (key: T:top, M:middle, B:bottom, L:left, R:right, C:centre)
Images in this book are copyright of the photographers and artists.

Maps – Torbay, UK 6TL, 6TR, 63 Dan Sutterby; 4TL, 27B, 49T spread, Kents Cavern; 4–5M, Glyn Thomas / Alamy; 5TR, BBC; 7, 26T, 26BL, 26BR,
26ML, 27TL, 27TR, 28–29, 30BR, 32T, 38–39, 40, 40TL, 41TR, 41B, 42BL, 43T, 46T, 54, 55TR, 57TL, 57B, 60, 61T, 61ML, 61MR, 61BL, 62BR, 64, English
Riviera Tourist Board; 8TR, Itiagowa Global Geopark; 8MR (upper), Kanawinka Global Geopark; 8MR (lower), Hong Kong Candidate Global
Geopark; 8BR, Yandangshan Global Geopark; 10–11 Mike McNally; 13, 13TR, 13ML, 19RM, 20BR, 42TL, 48TR, 51 inset MR, 52MR, 52ML, 57TL, 58T,
M. Border; 13BL, 35TR, 40TR, 47ML, TCCT; 13BR, 50T, 51, 51 inset TR, 55TL, Torquay Museum; 14TR, D. Larkin; 14MR, 14BL, 18–19, 21T, 18–19T,
25TL, 49ML, 58T inset, 59T, Chris Proctor; 15T, Brin Edwards; 15BR, 16–17T, 16BL, 16BR, 17MR, British Geological Survey © NERC; 20TR, Anna
Keheher; 21ML, James Bellchamber; 23TR, 31T, Torbay Library Services; 30T, 30T inset, 46 inset, Torre Abbey Collection; 31ML, W. Lawrence,
Devon SFC; 32BR, Jerry Burman; 33T, Vaughan Ryall / Alamy; 34T, 59BR, Dreamstime; 34BL, 34BR, 35MR, N .Smallbones; 35BR, 42TR, Dan Bolt; 36T
spread, Matthew Jones, Imagemakers; 36MR, Dave Porter / Alamy; 37T inset, M. Darlaston; 44–45 full spread, Ali Powe; 47T, Bridgeman Art
Library; 52T, www.sealmages.co.uk / Alamy; 53T, Natural History Museum; 56T, Stuart Murdoch; 56BR, J. Kaczanow; 57ML, Mike Langman; 59BR,
West Country Publications; 59BL, The Seahorse Trust; 62TL, Davy Cooper; 62TR, North West Highlands Geopark; 62BL, Charley Hedley/Natural
England; 62BR, GeoMon; 63TL, Lochaber Geopark; 63TR, Marble Arch Caves; 63BL, BBNPA; 63BR Copper Coast Geopark; 36BR, Gordon Thomas.

Front cover image © Mike McNally, www.mikemcnallyphotography.co.uk
All other artwork and diagrams, including title page and back cover: Bex Glover.
Fold-out map: Fruition Creative Services.
Geology map of the English Riviera Global Geopark with key British Geological Survey © NERC

The production of this guidebook had been kindly funded by:

Contents

ACKNOWLEDGEMENTS

Acknowledgements

This wonderful guide book truly shows the English Riviera Global Geopark at its best and why it's such a remarkable place to live in and visit. Many local people have had an influence on making this publication happen, in particular Dominic Acland, Georgina Bowen, Dave Butt, Sue Cheriton, Tina Crowson and Carolyn Custerson.

We would like to thank Dr Adrian Humpage at the British Geological Survey, Dr Jonathon Larwood at Natural England and Prof. Iain Stewart of Plymouth University for helping out with the technical sections and also Dr Chris Proctor and John Risdon for providing specialist written contributions to the geological and historical content.

However, one person in particular has put in more hard work and energy than anyone else and so we would like to express our gratitude to Melanie Border, the English Riviera Global Geopark Coordinator, whose dedication has been outstanding.

Nick Powe
Chairman of the
English Riviera Global Geopark

English Riviera

GLOBAL GEOPARK

Foreword

At first glance, the crowded shores of the English Riviera would seem an unlikely scene to create a Geopark. But amid the scattered urban mosaic of Brixham, Paignton and Torquay – tucked away in valleys, on hilltops, along blood-red bluffs or steel-grey sea stacks – is some of the best geology in southern Britain. Although not hidden from view, it is a legacy that for most people lies out of sight. The keys for revealing these geological foundations lie in these pages, which provide the means to unravel 400 million years of planetary change. Who would have thought that rocks laid down in Caribbean coral seas or Saharan desert dunes would now nestle so innocently in the gentle coastal scenery of the English Riviera? But there is more to this Geopark than simply a fascinating window into our planet's distant heritage. The resonance of these truly ancient roots endure in the modern make-up of this intricate coast – its architecture and buildings, its cultural and artistic roots, its creation of a sense of region and place. Simply, the Geopark is where people, rocks and landscapes meet.

Professor Iain Stewart, Plymouth University Patron of the English Riviera Global Geopark and presenter of BBC TV's How Earth Made Us *and* Earth: The Power of the Planet.

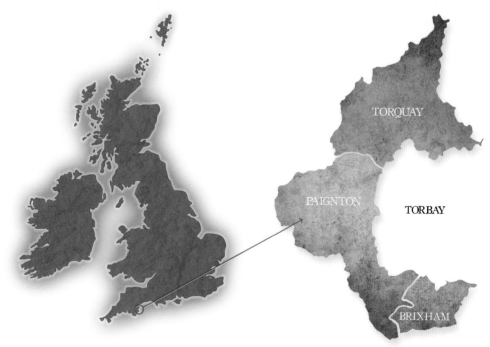

Welcome to the English Riviera Global Geopark...

...and the spectacular geological tale behind a dramatic and beautiful landscape which reveals incredible stories about our Earth's distant past. Here is a place that bears witness to tropical seas, scorching deserts, raised beaches and drowned forests; mammoths, sabre-toothed cats, cave bears and early man.

In September 2007 the English Riviera became the world's first urban Geopark and was welcomed as a member of the Global Geoparks Network with the support of UNESCO.* The bay's impressive geology, long taken for granted, is today recognised to be of international significance. Despite its urban setting, the English Riviera Global Geopark contains one of the highest concentrations of protected geological sites in the UK. There are 11 nationally protected Sites of Special Scientific Interest (SSSIs) and 16 Local Geological Sites, also known as Regionally Important Geological Sites (RIGS).

The English Riviera Global Geopark is a beautiful bay situated on the south coast of Devon, combining the towns of Brixham, Paignton, Torquay and Babbacombe. The area is often referred to as Torbay by local people. Stretching from the rolling hills inland out across the rich marine environment, the Geopark covers 64km^2 of land and 40km^2 of sea.

Such a rich geological heritage has influenced the area's remarkably diverse marine and terrestrial biodiversity, and shaped its incredible human history, from the earliest cave dwellers at Kents Cavern through to the tourism industry of today. The rocks beneath our feet continue to affect all aspects of our everyday lives, from local produce to the materials used for buildings, and from landscape to the economy. It is this earth heritage that lies at the heart of our Geopark.

Like other Geoparks within the Global Network we aim to enhance public awareness, understanding and appreciation of the natural world and the culture of the area. Geoparks promote sustainable forms of economic development, such as green tourism, so that future generations can continue to enjoy the wonders of our heritage.

This guide has been designed to help you explore the English Riviera Global Geopark and learn about the incredible stories of the past that can be unlocked from the landscape and heritage seen today.

* UNESCO – United Nations Educational, Scientific and Cultural Organisation.

Sailing in Tor Bay with Berry Head in the background

WELCOME

The European and Global Geoparks Network

If the story of the planet was compiled in a book then each individual Geopark would be able to contribute its own unique part of the tale. For some that might be just a few particularly significant pages but for others it would require several chapters to cover great chunks of geological time.

Founded in 2000, the European Geoparks Network (EGN) was initiated by just four areas: Réserve Géologique de Haute Provence (France), the Petrified Forest of Lesvos (Greece), Vulkaneifel - (Germany) and Maestrazgo Cultural Park (Spain). By 2004 the success of the EGN was recognised and this led to the global development of the network. This network has gone from strength to strength and, as of May 2010, the Global Geoparks Network comprises a total of 67 members across 19 member states.

Although a relative youngster within the network, the English Riviera Geopark on Devon's south coast is not only developing at a local level but is already well regarded internationally. As the first urban Geopark, the English Riviera is quite distinct from the rest of the world's Geoparks. These unique benefits and challenges provide experiences from which others can learn and it was this that led to the development of a relationship with the candidate Global Geopark in Hong Kong. In support of their application to join the network the English Riviera signed a partnership agreement with Hong Kong in November 2009, along with three other Global Geoparks, Kanawinka in Australia, Yandangshan in China and Itoigawa in Japan.

Today, working together as a global partnership with common goals, the network includes some of the most stunning places of natural beauty in the world, in countries as diverse as Australia, Brazil, China, Iran and Malaysia.

To discover more about Geoparks visit:
www.globalgeopark.org
or **www.europeangeoparks.org**

Kotaki Jade Gorge, Itoigawa Global Geopark, Japan

Tumuli, Kanawinka Global Geopark, Australia

Tolo Channel, Hong Kong Candidate Global Geopark

Yandangshan Global Geopark, China

European Geoparks Network Members List (May 2010)

1 Réserve Géologique de Haute Provence **FRANCE**
2 Vulkaneifel European Geopark **GERMANY**
3 Petrified Forest of Lesvos **GREECE**
4 Maestrazgo Cultural Park **SPAIN**
5 Psiloritis Nature Park **GREECE**
6 Terra.Vita Nature Park **GERMANY**
7 Copper Coast Geopark **IRELAND**
8 Marble Arch Caves European Geopark,
   Northern Ireland **UK**
9 Madonie Geopark **ITALY**
10 Rocca di Cerere **ITALY**
11 Nature Park Steirische Eisenwurzen **AUSTRIA**
12 Nature Park Bergstrasse Odenwald **GERMANY**
13 North Pennines AONB and European Geopark
   England **UK**
14 Park Naturel Régional du Luberon **FRANCE**
15 North West Highlands, Scotland **UK**
16 Geopark Swabian Albs **GERMANY**
17 Geopark Harz Braunschweiger Land Ostfalen
   Geopark **GERMANY**
18 Hateg Country Dinosaurs Geopark **ROMANIA**
19 Beigua Geopark **ITALY**
20 Fforest Fawr Geopark, Wales **UK**
21 Bohemian Paradise Geopark **CZECH REPUBLIC**

22 Cabo de Gata, Nijar Nature Park **SPAIN**
23 Naturtejo Geopark **PORTUGAL**
24 Sierras Subbeticas Nature Park **SPAIN**
25 Sobrarbe Geopark **SPAIN**
26 Gea Norvegica **NORWAY**
27 Geological Mining Park of Sardinia **ITALY**
28 Papuk Geopark **CROATIA**
29 Lochaber Geopark, Scotland **UK**
30 English Riviera Geopark, England **UK**
31 Adamello, Brenta Nature Park **ITALY**
32 Geo Mon, Wales **UK**
33 Arouca Geopark **PORTUGAL**
34 Geopark Shetland, Scotland **UK**
35 Chelmos Vouraikos **GREECE**
36 Novohrad-Nogad Geopark **HUNGARY/SLOVAKIA**
37 Magma Geopark **NORWAY**

Geoparks

GLOBAL
GEOPARKS
NETWORK

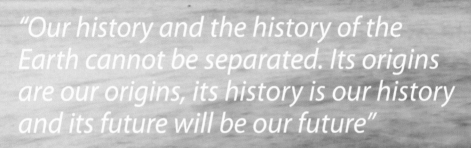

"Our history and the history of the Earth cannot be separated. Its origins are our origins, its history is our history and its future will be our future"

ProGEO, Digne Declaration, Declaration of the Rights of the Memory of the Earth

An Introduction to the History of the Planet

In the grand scheme of things our impression that we are standing on solid ground is deceptive. The Earth is dynamic both inside and out. An understanding of the geological processes in operation from the very beginning helps to explain why the geology we find around us today is how it is. Having formed as part of the Solar System around 4.6 billion years ago, the internal structure of the earth is composed of concentric layers.

At extremely high temperature and pressure, the densest part of the Earth is the solid inner core, which is surrounded by a semi-liquid outer core. The coolest, lightest and thinnest part of the Earth is the outermost layer, the crust. In between core and crust is a thick layer known as the mantle – solid rock capable of slow movement like treacle. The movement of the mantle is key to the changes that have occurred on the Earth's surface since its formation.

The Earth's crust moves with the underlying mantle in great slabs, known as plates. The plates fit together like a giant jigsaw, each piece constantly moving relative to another. Known as plate tectonics, this process is responsible for continents colliding and pulling apart as they move around the surface of the globe. Oceans open and close, sea levels dramatically alter and mountain ranges rise and fall. The result is millions of years of restlessness – explosive volcanic action, great earthquakes and huge pressures disrupt and contort the rock strata below our feet.

The story of the earth is divided into geological time periods and the rocks of the English Riviera Global Geopark reveal tantalising glimpses into parts of this remarkable past:

Devonian
The warm and inviting tropical seas of the Devonian Period around 400 million years ago.

Devonian solitary coral fossil

Carboniferous
A colossal mountain-building event that took place roughly 300 million years ago, the result of two major continents colliding.

Folded and fractured rock at Berry Head, Brixham

Permian
A desolate desert environment during the Permian Period, approximately 280 million years ago.

Permian deposits at Roundham Head, Paignton

Quaternary
And finally a time of major climate change and the advent of man during the relatively recent Quaternary Period which continues today.

Neanderthal Mousterian handaxe from Kents Cavern, Torquay

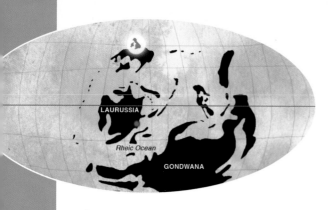

Thamnopora coral fossil, Hope's Nose, Torquay

The Devonian Story

In an environment somewhat similar to the Caribbean today, the first part of the geological story of the English Riviera begins, around 400 million years ago, close to the southern edge of a continent called Laurussia within the Rheic Ocean. Despite the somewhat fictional-sounding names, it was here that our earliest rocks were formed in an environment far to the south of where we are today; in fact the Geopark was south of the equator. Since this time, plate movements have taken us northwards.

Goniatite, Saltern Cove, Paignton

The sediments that formed our oldest rocks, slates and sandstones, were deposited in shallow seas. Later, the sea floor subsided unevenly. In shallow water, banks and reefs of limestone formed. At the same time volcanic islands grew and their eruptions periodically blanketed the reefs in ash. Between the reefs and islands, slates were deposited in deeper water.

By this point in the Earth's history, the evolution of life was well under way but the corals that bind modern reefs together had yet to evolve. Our Devonian reef was built of hard sponges known as stromatoporoids. In the quieter, more sheltered backwaters, early corals did thrive, along with a wealth of exotic life now long extinct. Sea lilies or crinoids, resembling upside-down

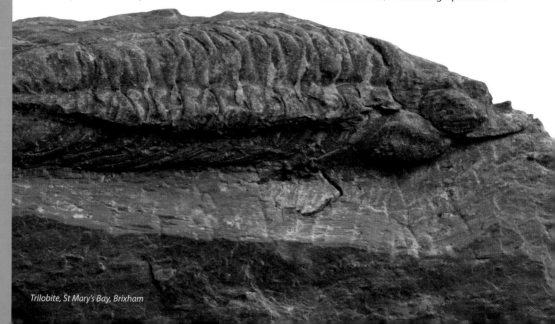

Trilobite, St Mary's Bay, Brixham

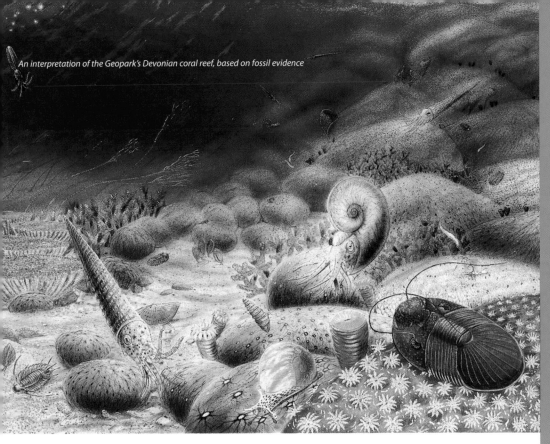

An interpretation of the Geopark's Devonian coral reef, based on fossil evidence

starfish on anchored flexible stems, drifted back and forth in the gentle currents. Giant woodlouse-like trilobites scuttled across the sea floor in search of their next meal, in turn being hunted by the cone-shaped nautiloids and coiled goniatites, early relatives of well-known ammonites, which are found along the Jurassic Coast World Heritage Site, to the east of us.

The corals, sponges, shells and skeletons of these creatures accumulated layer upon layer on the sea bed and were compressed over millions of years by younger sediments deposited on top to form hard limestone.

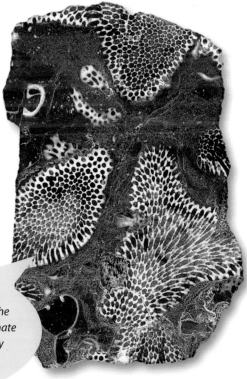

Look out for...

our two limestone headlands, Hope's Nose to the north and Berry Head to the south, which dominate the bay and Devonian fossils, which can easily be seen in limestone pebbles on the beach and in the sea walls.

Thamnopora cervicornus, a fossil coral

Part of William Smith's 1815 geological map

Sir Henry De La Beche (1796–1855)

Roderick Murchison (1792–1871)

Devonian Controversy

The founder of the British Geological Survey, Sir Henry De la Beche, carried out an early part of his pioneering work by mapping and describing the geology of the Torbay district. He published an extended account 'On the geology of Tor and Babbacombe bays' in 1829 and this formed a model for the subsequent geological work that resulted in the establishment of the national survey.

However, by the late 1830s, when Victorian scientists were developing a system for naming the principal periods of geological time, De la Beche's interpretation of Torbay and the overall mapping and interpretation of the geological strata of Devon were the cause of heated debates. Arguments ensued which occupied the members of the Geological Society in London. The leading geologists and protagonists of the debate, Roderick Murchison and Adam Sedgwick, had mapped strata in Wales and established the classic 'Silurian' (443–416 million years ago) and 'Cambrian' (542–488 million years ago) systems. They simply did not believe the results of mapping undertaken by De la Beche here in Devon of what were considered rocks of similar age. This led to a very public disagreement in the national media. After much mud-slinging and maligning of each other, recognition of the rich

Adam Sedgwick (1785–1873)

fossil fauna found in the limestone at sites in the bay, such as Lummaton Quarry in 1839, made an important contribution to an understanding of what was happening on Earth around 416–359 million years ago. Largely through Murchison's own scientific re-interpretation, the period of geological time named the 'Devonian' was proposed, inspired by the county in which the fossils were located. This debate became known as the Devonian Controversy. The name Devonian was soon used globally to identify all rocks and fossils of a similar age.

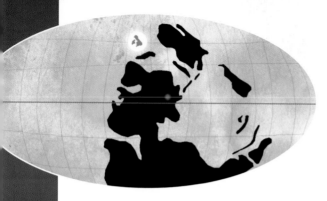

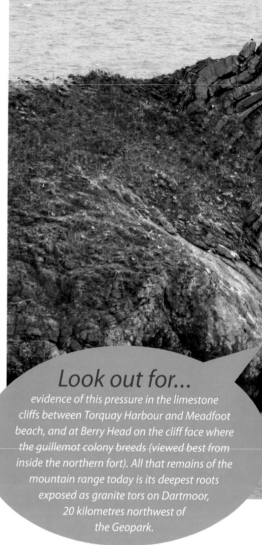

Continental Collision

Around 300 million years ago, in a time period called the Carboniferous, the tropical waters of the Devonian seas were a distant memory. The limestone formed during the Devonian was caught in the middle of a major collision as it crossed the equator.

The ongoing process of plate tectonics caused two continents, Laurussia and Gondwana, to its south, to collide as they slowly moved north, resulting in the birth of a supercontinent called Pangaea, which combined all of the Earth's land masses. Heralded by volcanic activity that had earlier caused ash to smother the reef systems, intense pressures eventually squeezed all the sediments that had been laid down in the Rheic Ocean, pushing and piling them up. The sheer scale and power of this event, known by geologists as the 'Variscan Orogeny', led to the formation of a vast mountain chain. The mountains would have stretched from eastern North America (which was joined to Europe at the time), through Cornwall and Devon to the Czech Republic and beyond.

Needless to say, this event had a fundamental effect on the rocks of the English Riviera. Sediments of Devonian age were folded and fractured as they were crumpled and pushed northwards by the collision.

Look out for...

evidence of this pressure in the limestone cliffs between Torquay Harbour and Meadfoot beach, and at Berry Head on the cliff face where the guillemot colony breeds (viewed best from inside the northern fort). All that remains of the mountain range today is its deepest roots exposed as granite tors on Dartmoor, 20 kilometres northwest of the Geopark.

Formation of the Ore Stone fold

Stage 1
Layers of limestone are deposited on the Devonian sea bed and harden to form rock.

Above: Evidence of folding on the island of Ore Stone, off Hope's Nose, Torquay

Right: Cliffs below Rock End, Torquay

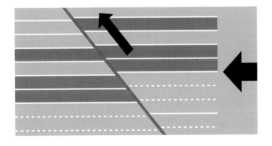

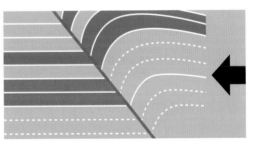

Stage 2

Pressure on the rocks during the Variscan Orogeny causes the limestone to fracture and one mass pushes over the other.

Stage 3

The fracture sticks but continued pressure forces the upper mass over further, forming a fold.

PANGAEA

were rapidly filled with desert sands. What was to become the location of Paignton lay in a broad valley with jagged ridges of limestone on either side and there were more valleys to the north, at Oddicombe and north of Petit Tor. These deposits form the starting point of the geological sequence recognised at the Jurassic Coast World Heritage Site.

The Permian Story

By the Permian, 280 million years ago, the harsh continental conditions in the heartland of Pangaea were taking their toll. Quickly the enormous mountain belt formed during the Carboniferous began to erode. The Devonian limestone which had formed millions of years earlier and been buried deep in the Variscan mountains was now exposed by erosion in an extreme desert environment, in the tropics north of the equator, at latitudes similar to the Sahara today. Plate tectonic movement started to pull the land apart, causing an area to the east of us to subside and become an open plain. Cracks and fissures developed in the limestone but these

Limestone crack filled with sandstone, Shoalstone, Brixham

Rare, violent storms caused flash floods to sweep stones and rocks down the desert valleys into the open plain. The water rapidly soaked into the parched rocky and sandy ground, dumping its load of sediments, which today forms a rock type called breccia.

Look out for...

our red Permian age rocks that can be seen all around the inner area of the bay. Gently curving diagonal lines in fine sandstone deposits reveal the profile of ancient wind-blown sand dunes while the more jumbled, lumpy breccia deposits were carried by water.

Professor Iain Stewart with students on Goodrington beach, Paignton

Desert sandstone at Roundham Head, Paignton

At times, wind- blown sand dunes were deposited during dry periods between the floods. Groundwater under the desert floor oxidised the iron within the sediments, converting it to the mineral haematite, and this explains the deep red colour of the rocks and Devon's classic red soil.

Fossilised burrow

Although conditions were harsh, there is fossil evidence of life. At sites around the bay, sands and small pebbles have been rearranged by a burrowing creature, but to date there has been no way of identifying what this creature was. Theories have ranged from giant sandworms to small reptiles, with the current favourite being giant millipedes. For now the mystery remains unsolved, but we can be sure that the creature became extinct, along with a multitude of other species at the end of the Permian.

At some point during the Permian and the next geological period, the Triassic, fluids rich in minerals flowed through the rocks. The reaction of the fluids with the Devonian limestone led to the formation of deposits of iron ore in the Brixham area. Different mineralising fluids led to the formation of mineral veins in the Devonian limestone of Hope's Nose.

What Happened Next?

During the Triassic, Jurassic, Cretaceous and Tertiary the area continues to move north and deposition, especially chalk, continued, but much of this has now been removed by erosion. So, our geological record becomes harder to follow until around 2 million years ago. That doesn't mean nothing was happening. We can sometimes glimpse traces of the events over this period that helped make the English Riviera the place it is today.

At the end of the Permian, a huge mass extinction occurred which wiped out 95 per cent of all life on Earth. Things slowly recovered and a twist in the evolutionary tale led to the domination and then the extinction, roughly 150 million years later, of the dinosaurs. Other important groups appeared, which fared rather better - the mammals, birds and flowering plants. Meanwhile, the ever-constant deep churning of the Earth's interior continued to drive the plate tectonic movements so that the Pangaea supercontinent broke up into smaller continents.

During the Jurassic the rocks that form the bay were temporarily on the coast of a verdant island, Cornubia. Evidence of the vegetation of Cornubia can be found at Lyme Regis in the form of fossil wood washed off the island. By the late Cretaceous, the whole area was drowned under the sea with the water possibly being as much as 250 metres above today's sea level.

Further continental collisions led to the formation of the Alps and the Himalayas. Although the major effects of the Alpine mountain-building phase are found in continental Europe, the rocks of this area fractured and faulted under the pressure. Fault lines criss-cross the bay.

Look out for...

the rock face of Royal Terrace Gardens at the northern end of the seafront, Torquay. This is where a large fault emerges and heads off out to sea, just passing Berry Head. Look across to the north end of Broadsands beach to see a fault separating grey Devonian limestone on the left from red Permian sandstone on the right.

Royal Terrace Gardens, Torquay during the early 1900s

Walk, Torquay, W.121

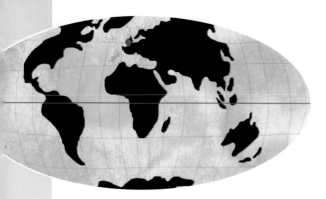

Climate Change in the Quaternary

During the last 2.6 million years, having moved close to its present latitude, Britain has been subjected to repeated glacial periods or ice ages divided by warm periods, known as interglacials. During glacial times, extensive ice sheets developed across northern Britain and Europe. So, while much of Britan was locked in ice the bay would have experienced very cold, tundra conditions, like northern Siberia today. Repeated freezing and thawing caused mud and fractured rock to slump down the slopes of hills. Sea levels would have been much lower during the ice ages, so the English Channel between Britain and France would not have existed, making it possible for people and animals to walk freely across the open plains. The intervening warm interglacials, saw elephants, rhinoceroses and even hippopotamuses munching on abundant vegetation. During the last interglacial period, about 125,000 years ago, it was probably warmer than today. Relatively high sea levels at this time left raised beaches such as the one at Hope's Nose.

During the Quaternary, rainwater and streams carved out caves in the limestone that was once again exposed. These caves became the home for wild animals such as hyenas, sabre-toothed cats and cave bears at a time when the climate was colder and the mammoths and woolly rhinoceroses roamed. Most famous for its rich deposits of ice-age mammal bones is Kents Cavern in Torquay, where human remains, as well as tools, are evidence of early human occupation dating back nearly 500,000 years.

Today we are living in the most recent interglacial period, called the Holocene, which began 10,000 years ago. Ice caps started to melt and by 7,000 years ago the sea had risen to its present-day level, flooding woodlands which had grown up on what is now the floor of the bay. The hard limestone of Berry Head and Hope's Nose has stood resisting erosion for hundreds of thousands of years, while the less resistant red sandstone rocks have been worn away, forming what we know today as the English Riviera.

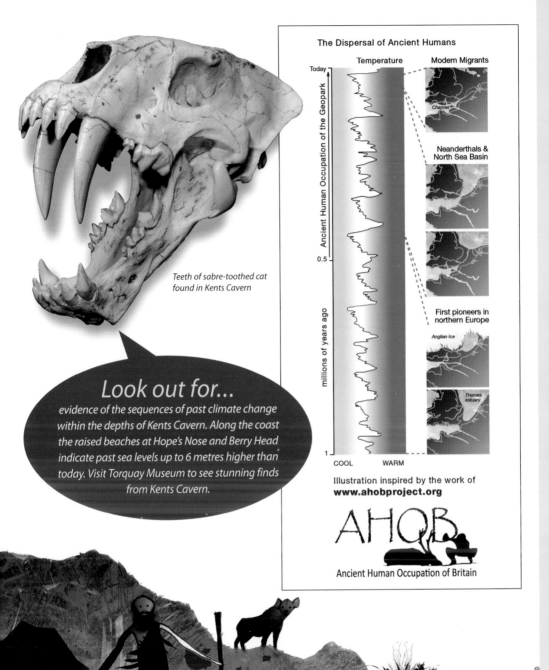

Teeth of sabre-toothed cat found in Kents Cavern

The Dispersal of Ancient Humans

Temperature — Modern Migrants

Channel

Neanderthals & North Sea Basin

First pioneers in northern Europe

Anglian Ice

Thames estuary

COOL — WARM

Ancient Human Occupation of the Geopark

millions of years ago

Today

0.5

1

Illustration inspired by the work of
www.ahobproject.org

AHQB

Ancient Human Occupation of Britain

Look out for...

evidence of the sequences of past climate change within the depths of Kents Cavern. Along the coast the raised beaches at Hope's Nose and Berry Head indicate past sea levels up to 6 metres higher than today. Visit Torquay Museum to see stunning finds from Kents Cavern.

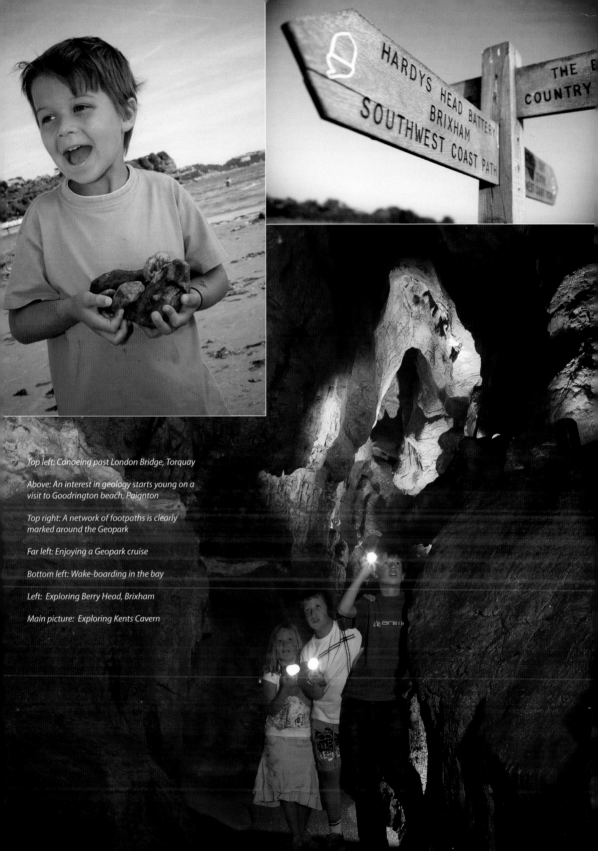

Top left: Canoeing past London Bridge, Torquay

Above: An interest in geology starts young on a visit to Goodrington beach, Paignton

Top right: A network of footpaths is clearly marked around the Geopark

Far left: Enjoying a Geopark cruise

Bottom left: Wake-boarding in the bay

Left: Exploring Berry Head, Brixham

Main picture: Exploring Kents Cavern

BRIXHAM

"Abide with me; fast falls eventide;
The darkness deepens; Lord, with me abide.
When other helpers fail and comforts flee,
Help of the helpless, O abide with me."

Reverend Henry Francis Lyte (1793 –1847). After giving his last service in Brixham, from his home, he penned his most famous hymn, Abide With Me, after watching the sun set over the bay.

Napoleon on board HMS Bellerophon

'Man of War in Torbay', 1809, by Thomas Luny

The Brixham Story

Before its twentieth-century expansion, Brixham nestled safely beneath the protective arm of Berry Head. It has been a town of two communities since medieval times. Its Saxon origins lie within sight of St Mary's Church, Higher Brixham, where the community's interests were largely associated with farming, hence the nickname 'Cow Town'.

By medieval times a second community associated with the activities of the sea had begun to develop around the nearby steep-sided inlet that ran east to west. To identify their activities within the expanding town of Brixham the harbour community became known as 'Fish Town'.

Brixham cottages

Brixham has developed into a significant fishing port, tucked into the southernmost part of the bay. The surrounding geology has provided shelter to these waters from the prevailing southwesterly winds and destructive gales.

The safe anchorage became renowned among mariners, both merchant and naval, and the Port of Brixham developed accordingly in commercial trade and fishery. On 5 November 1688 its facilities would be recognised with the landing of the Dutch Prince William of Orange and his army. Having encamped on Furzeham Common, then outside the town, William began his advance on London to claim the British throne.

Norwegian ice ships in Brixham Harbour bringing Arctic ice to keep the fish fresh during late Victorian times

Brixham fishing boat

Top 5 things to do in Brixham...

- Visit Berry Head, Gateway Site for the Geopark, to explore the new visitor centre and enjoy the exceptional views
- Stroll around the vibrant fish market
- Head out to sea on a Geopark cruise
- See the Heritage Fleet in the harbour
- Step on board the *Golden Hind* museum ship, and enter the world of Sir Francis Drake

By the time of Nelson and the Napoleonic Wars, the anchorage of Brixham had become a great favourite for the Channel fleet. The fleet, made up of over 20,000 men, used to replenish their supplies of fresh water and provisions under the protection of the guns up on Berry Head. Prior to his exile at the end of the conflict, in 1815, Napoleon was held prisoner on HMS *Bellerophon*, at anchor in the bay. It is rumoured that when he was allowed on deck, he likened the bay to the Mediterranean south coast of France, which later, in Victorian times, gave rise to the title of the English Riviera.

As time progressed on through the reign of Queen Victoria, Brixham craftsmen and fishermen would be at the forefront of innovation within the fishing trade. The Brixham trawler was the first vessel built strong enough to pull a net-full of fish in a strong wind. Brixham became the mother port of trawling.

To provide landing facilities and improved shelter for the ever-increasing fishing fleet the harbour was extended. The last major extension to enclose the harbour was the outer breakwater, 1kilometre in length, completed in 1916. The stone required for this was Devonian limestone and it was provided from Freshwater Quarry, now a car park, on the opposite side of the outer harbour.

The Heritage Fleet in Tor Bay

Lime kiln in The Grove, Brixham

Brixham Mining and Quarrying

Considerable deposits of iron ore have been found within the Devonian limestone that extends from the Brixham area through to Churston, Galmpton and the Dart estuary. During Victorian times this ore was highly regarded and a number of mines developed. One was at Sharkham Head, where the ore was directly loaded onto ships for transportation to the smelters at Swansea in South Wales.

Another associated mineral was iron ochre, with significant deposits found in and around Brixham, especially up on Furzeham Common, where open-cast pits were worked. Using the ochre, Richard Wolston, local businessman and mine owner, developed the first rust-resistant paint ever made. The foundations of his paint

The ruin of Lord Churston's bathhouse, Elberry Cove, Brixham

factory, adjacent to Freshwater car park, can still be seen.

The red ochre was also used in a preparation to help preserve the fishermen's canvas sails, giving them a tan colour, from which the song 'Red Sails in the Sunset' originates.

The Devonian limestone in the cliffs at Elberry Cove has been quarried in the Seven Sisters Quarries. The stone was used for building and also for conversion into lime. Within the nearby woods, The Grove, are the remains of lime kilns, in which stone was converted into quicklime and then into slaked lime, if required. These products were used for a multitude of purposes, from 'sweetening' or fertilising soil, to making lime mortar for building.

Elberry Cove stands out due to its storm ridge of bleached limestone pebbles. At its southern end lie the ruins of Lord Churston's bathhouse, originally thought to have been a pilchard smoke house. Muslim leader Ali Khan married the daughter of Lord Churston and their son the Aga Khan was born in 1936. Here Lord Churston and his guests could 'take the waters', in heated salt-water baths, for their health.

Main picture: The guillemot colony at Berry Head is regularly a thousand or so birds strong

Bottom left: Bee orchid

Bottom right: Greater knapweed

Right top: Guillemots do not build nests so the rocky ledges provide the ideal place to lay their single egg

Right middle: Within the short limestone grassland a multitude of rare plant species thrive

Right bottom: Hidden beneath the waves, the wealth of sea caves provides a home for wonderful and strange marine animals

Berry Head – Geopark Gateway Site and National Nature Reserve

Excellently explained in the visitor centre, Berry Head boasts an impressive list of official designations, all of which reflect its national and international significance for nature conservation.

Clinging to the thin limestone soils are around 500 plant species, a good number of them nationally rare. There are 28 species of butterfly, including the distinctly uncommon 'common blue', and hundreds of other insect species.

The mix of grassland, scrub woodland and rocky nooks and crannies provides a variety of habitats for birds. About 200 species have been recorded and 50 species, including the nationally threatened cirl bunting, breed within or close to the National Nature Reserve. The cliffs are host to the largest breeding colony of guillemots on the south coast of England – regularly a thousand birds strong. And that's just the wildlife above ground!

Hiding in the dark recesses of Berry Head's caves is one of Britain's most endangered mammals. As well as being one of the rarest, it is also one of the largest of its kind, with a 35-centimetre wingspan. The roosting colony of greater horseshoe bats here on Berry Head is one of the most fragile and threatened in the country.

Meanwhile, the caves at sea level are home to some rare species of marine fauna, such as pink sea fingers and carpet coral. However, the caves are not just a home for rare species. Research by expert cavers and divers, both above and below current sea level, has revealed that they provide a unique record of sea-level changes from 350,000 years ago to the present.

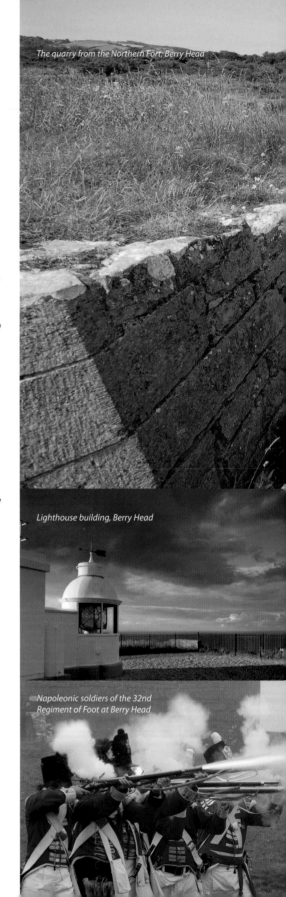

The quarry from the Northern Fort, Berry Head

Lighthouse building, Berry Head

Napoleonic soldiers of the 32nd Regiment of Foot at Berry Head

Berry Head – The Human Influence

Towering 60 metres above the English Channel, the headland has acted as a landmark, perfect lookout and natural fortification since the Iron Age, with the Romans using the site as a signal station during their long occupation of Britain.

Lying abandoned on the northern flank of Berry Head is a vast limestone quarry – the culmination of over 300 years of quarrying. The quarry was in its heyday during the 1930s, 40s and 50s, with production in some years exceeding 200,000 tons.

The most obvious but much older products of the quarry can be seen in the ramparts of the two Napoleonic forts. These were built to defend a battery of guns positioned on the tip of the headland, there to protect the fleet at anchor in the sheltered waters below from the French. A number of interesting buildings remain associated with this era, such as the guardhouse at Berry Head, which now houses a Geopark visitor centre and café.

The incredible purity of the limestone (nearly 99 per cent calcium carbonate) has long made Berry Head important to agriculture, industry and construction. Extracted lime was used to make fertiliser, mortar and cement, and was also exported as smelting lime for use in the iron-making industry. Block-cut and chipped stone was used for road building, including infrastructure to support the D-Day campaign in 1944, and in the construction of notable buildings in South Devon and further afield.

So extensive are the workings that in places the floor of the quarry is actually below sea level. Quarry workers uncovered a network of caves and passages that wind their way into the heart of the headland.

Today, the quiet seclusion of the quarry makes it ideal for nesting seabirds and hunting peregrine falcons, while at the end of the headland the smallest but tallest lighthouse in the country, built in 1906, continues to keep mariners safe.

Peregrine falcon in the quarry

Walking Trail at Berry Head

Harbour
Freshwater
Brixham Marina
Fishing Port

Breakwater Beach
Shoalstone Sea Water Pool
Shoalstone Beach

Berry Head Rd
Heath Rd

King St
Rea Barn Rd
Ranscombe Rd
Higher Ranscombe Rd
Gillard Rd

Bolton St

Berry Head Country Park & National Nature Reserve

North Fort

Lighthouse
Berry Head

Visitor Centre

Start

Southern Fort

Durl Head

St Mary's
St Mary's Bay

Sharkham Point
Sharkham Point

N

Follow the
Berry Head Geo Trail
Pick up a trail leaflet
at the Berry Head
Visitor Centre

THE HUMAN INFLUENCE

PAIGNTON

"My family has never tried to persuade me to holiday anywhere else – they all love it here."

Dick Francis (1910–2010), crime writer and champion jockey, on his 50-year love affair with holidaying in Paignton.

Paignton Pier

Occombe Farm, Paignton

Broadsands beach, Paignton

Top 5 things to do in Paignton...

- Visit the Seashore Centre, Goodrington, Gateway Site for the Geopark
- Build sandcastles on the beach. The texture of our red sand has been shown to be the best in the country for this
- Head inland to connect with farming, nature and great food at Occombe Farm
- For fantastic views take a trip on the Steam Railway
- Have fun rock-pooling at Goodrington

The Paignton Story

The Saxons first developed the town that would become Paignton on a shelf of land, 1.5 kilometres inland from the sea. The centre of that early community is beautifully highlighted by the Permian red sandstone tower of the Parish Church of St John. Close by is the Coverdale tower, also of red sandstone. Saxon in origin, the tower was part of the defences of the Bishop's Palace, indicating both the appeal of Paignton in those days and the threat of Vikings from the sea. The Tower is named after Bishop Myles Coverdale, who compiled and published the first modern English translation of the Bible in 1536. Coverdale was Bishop of Exeter between 1551 and 1553.

By the time of the Norman Domesday Book, Paignton was the wealthiest manor within the bounds of Torbay, due to its agriculture and salt workings. With the arrival of the railway in 1859 Paignton began its transformation into a family seaside resort. By 1866 the sea wall and promenade had been completed where there had once been sand dunes. Behind this an area of salt-water marsh and meadow was developed into Paignton Green and an elegant Victorian new town. The pier was opened in 1879.

For centuries the beach was where boats would

Coverdale Tower, Paignton

'beach' on the high tide to allow the loading and unloading of cargoes, including contraband. In 1838 the present harbour, to the south end of the beach, was improved to allow ships to take out great quantities of locally made cider. Bisecting the three kilometres of beach, dividing Paignton from Preston Sands, is a ridge of rock on which Redcliffe Towers was built during the 1850s. Designed by its owner, Colonel Robert Smith, a retired Indian Army engineer and architect, it reflects his association with his earlier life.

The long sandy beaches in Paignton are what has made the town such a popular holiday destination for generations of families.

Fresco at Bishop's Palace, Paignton

The Seashore Centre, Paignton

Tompot blenny

The Seashore Centre – Geopark Gateway Site

The Seashore Centre at Goodrington, Paignton, provides a great starting point to explore the coastal life of the bay both past and present. Meanwhile, low tide on Goodrington beach reveals what is reputed to be one of the best sites in the country for rock-pooling. The beach is neighboured by two protected sites, Roundham Head Site of Special Scientific Interest (SSSI) to the north and Saltern Cove SSSI to the south, which is also the first marine Local Nature Reserve to be designated in the country.

Enjoying the Saltern Cove Trail, Paignton

A wander to the end of South Beach will link the walker of today with a traumatic event of the past. Here the jagged and jumbled rocks are evidence of a dramatic flash flood that swept down from distant mountains some 270 million years ago. Gathering speed and strength, rough-edged chunks of rock were picked up and carried along with the flow to be dumped as the water spread out across an open plain during the Permian.

At low tide a ramble further along the rocky shore will take you past the Permian fossilised burrows, direct to Saltern Cove. It is here that you can view a major gap in time! The lower cliff is early Devonian, 400 million years old, and the Permian that sit on top are about 270 million years old. Logically, Carboniferous rocks should be found in between but these were all eroded away, so all we find now is a 218-million -year-old desert ground surface at the contact point. This feature is known by geologists as an unconformity.

Running along the coastline from Goodrington to Broadsands and beyond is an evocative length of railway line. Surveyed and designed by Isambard Kingdom Brunel, it was completed by 1861 to carry trains on the main line to the port of Dartmouth at Kingswear. Still in use today, the Steam Railway provides spectacular views. With numerous cuttings and embankments, the major engineering feat included the construction of two stone viaducts using local Devonian limestone which remain as majestic today as when they were built.

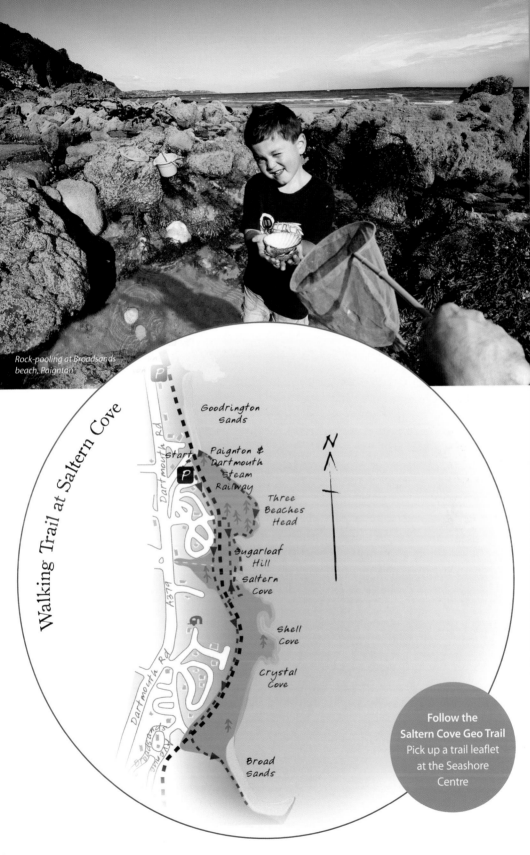

Rock-pooling at Broadsands beach, Paignton

Walking Trail at Saltern Cove

Goodrington
Sands

Start

Paignton &
Dartmouth
Steam
Railway

Three
Beaches
Head

Sugarloaf
Hill

Saltern
Cove

Shell
Cove

Crystal
Cove

Broad
Sands

Dartmouth Rd

A379

Dartmouth Rd

N

**Follow the
Saltern Cove Geo Trail**
Pick up a trail leaflet
at the Seashore
Centre

TORQUAY

"The caves... were very easy to explore and only moderately damp. Papa got dirty... and slipped off a board into the sticky red clay."

Beatrix Potter (1866–1943) describing her visit to Kents Cavern, 14 March 1893

The 800-year-old Torre Abbey, Torquay

Medieval undercroft at Torre Abbey

The Torquay Story

Present-day Torquay is made up of a number of ancient Saxon manors and Cockington, situated in a hidden valley, still retains a rural identity. The Cockington estate was sold to the council during the 1930s and since the Second World War has become a Country Park, complete with village, church and court. After a thousand years of ownership by the gentry, it now reflects the rural traditions and creative crafts of South Devon in beautiful surroundings.

To the north of Cockington lies the ancient manor of Torre, with its centrepiece, Torre Abbey, the oldest building in the bay. The abbey was built in the late twelfth century for an order of canons often referred to as the White Monks and became one of the wealthiest abbeys in the country. Considerable quantities of local Devonian limestone from the bay and Permian sandstone from nearby Corbyn's Head were used in its construction.

Following the Dissolution of the Monasteries by Henry VIII, the abbey became a private residence, but not before its tithe barn had been used as a

Top 5 things to do in Torquay...

- Explore Britain's oldest prehistoric dwelling at Kents Cavern, Gateway Site for the Geopark
- Enjoy an amazing view of the bay from the viewing platform at the Royal Terrace Gardens on the seafront
- Soak up the atmosphere and admire the art in the ancient Torre Abbey
- Head out to sea on a Geopark cruise
- See local craftspeople at work then relax in the grounds of Cockington Court

'Torquay Harbour', c.1830 (oil on canvas) by John Rawson Walker (1796–1873), on display at Torre Abbey

Cockington Court, Cockington, Torquay

out into the town of Torquay during Georgian times and on through into the nineteenth century, developing around the little harbour which gave meaning to its name.

Torquay developed as a winter resort for the aristocracy and gentry because of its mild climate. Geology, geography and climate all came together to provide the perfect setting and Italianate-style villas were built by the Cary and Palk families for the wealthy to lease. A major attraction was the sea, allowing people to 'take the waters' for the good of their health. Only later did sea bathing become popular as a recreation, so initially heated salt-water baths had to be constructed for medicinal purposes.

Queen Victoria visited and gave the area her 'stamp of approval' and soon Torquay became the most popular resort in the country for the upper classes. Visitors came from abroad too, so the arrival of an American gentleman, Frederick Miller, with his English wife was not unusual. They decided to make Torquay their home and it was here in September 1890 that their third child Agatha was born. She would later become famous as Agatha Christie.

temporary prison for Spanish prisoners from the Armada in 1588, and hence it became known as the Spanish Barn. From the eighteenth century up until the 1930s it was the home of the Cary family, one of the founding families of Torquay. The recently restored abbey is now a major tourist attraction and includes stimulating, ever-changing art exhibits.

From its original name of Torre (signifying a rocky crag), the village eventually began to blossom

Kents Cavern – Geopark Gateway Site and Scheduled Ancient Monument

Undoubtedly Kents Cavern is one of the most special show caves in the country. The cave's incredible geology and rich archaeological heritage have been astounding scientists and visitors alike for centuries. Records show the mysteries of the caves have been enticing explorers to venture into their depths since 1571. However, archaeological evidence and research reveal that people and animals have been visiting the caves almost continually for hundreds of thousands of years.

The caves began to form around 2.5 million years ago when cavities started to open up in the limestone rock that now contains Kents Cavern. Limestone is composed of calcium carbonate, which is soluble in acids. As rainwater, turned acidic by carbon dioxide, moved down through cracks the very rock itself was slowly dissolved away through a chemical reaction that widened crevices to form caves and passages.

After the caves formed, mud and rocks gradually worked their way through the system. During warm periods, dripping water evaporated to deposit calcium carbonate in the form of stalactites hanging from the ceiling, stalagmites growing up from the floor and layers of flowstone coating the walls and floor. Caves filled up, remains of animals, from the smallest of voles to enormous woolly rhinoceroses, and of our ancient ancestors who took refuge in the caves were buried between the layers of mud and stalagmite floors building up.

The earliest inhabitants were cave bears, which used the caves to hibernate and give birth. Later, during the last ice age, the cave became a hyena den. Ice-age hyenas were larger than modern hyenas, and as well as scavenging were capable of killing the largest prey and even resorted to cannibalism. The cave earth of Kents Cavern is full of the bones of hyenas and the animals they ate, including woolly rhinoceroses, mammoths, horses, reindeers and other creatures of the ice-age world.

Formation of Kents Cavern

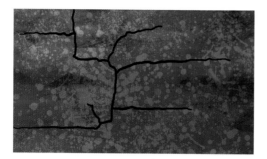

Stage 1
After millions of years of geological pressure as continents collided and pulled apart the limestone rock around the bay was full of cracks.

Stage 2
Erosion exposed the limestone. Rainwater turned acidic by carbon dioxide entered the cracks. The weak acid started to dissolve the limestone and the process of cave formation began.

KENTS CAVERN

The caves have an incredible record of human activity from all three stages of the Old Stone Age (Palaeolithic) stretching back roughly 500,000 years. Handaxes made by the earliest inhabitants are found in the same deposits as the cave bears. The lower part of the cave earth contains tools left by Neanderthal man, who lived in and hunted around the cave 40–50,000 years ago. After the Neanderthals disappeared, the cave was inhabited by early modern humans. The most important find is a human jawbone dated at 37–40,000 years old, recently confirmed as the oldest anatomically modern human fossil in Europe.

The caves, Britain's oldest recognisable human dwelling, are now an award-winning attraction and are open all year for excellent guided tours.

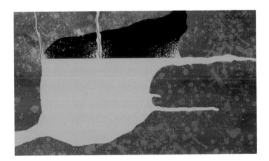

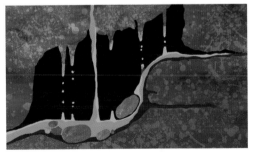

Stage 3
Cracks widened, a stream ran through the flooded cave and the water became faster and more turbulent. Erosion, a powerful force, created a network of passages, caves and chambers.

Stage 4
During the ice ages the water flow ceased but in intervening warm periods water seeped through again and drip by drip layers of stalagmite formed, entombing evidence of occupation.

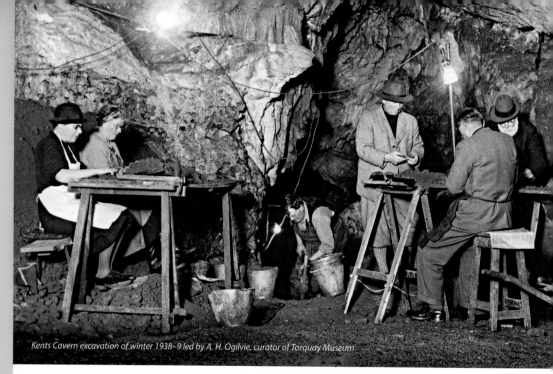

Kents Cavern excavation of winter 1938–9 led by A. H. Ogilvie, curator of Torquay Museum

Antiquity of Man

By the mid eighteenth century, the age of the Earth was calculated by working through historical records and the Bible. This gave a date of 4004 BC for the creation of the world including humans. The subsequent study of rocks showed that the Earth had to be much older and by the early nineteenth century scientists were starting to investigate when humans actually appeared.

Kents Cavern would have remained just another hole in the ground had it not been for the remarkable work of two men. The first was Father John MacEnery, a Roman Catholic priest to the Cary family living at Torre Abbey, who was encouraged by the Oxford geologist William Buckland to excavate in the cave between 1825 and 1829. MacEnery unearthed the first finds of flint tools together with the bones of extinct animals from the same level under ancient stalagmite floors. The geological age of the floors meant that his discoveries of human activity in the cave could be much older than 4004 BC, challenging his own beliefs as a devout Catholic. Buckland and others persuaded MacEnery that these human artefacts could only have been placed in the cave in modern times and he abandoned his research.

Thirty years later William Pengelly, a teacher from Looe in Cornwall, came to Torquay as a private tutor. Inspired by MacEnery's work, he carried out an excavation in Kents Cavern between 1865 and 1880. He was well aware of the controversial nature of his work and so was scientifically meticulous in recording the excavation. He invented the archaeological grid system of recording finds. By candlelight a small team, helped by Topsy the donkey, removed two stalagmite floors. Sealed beneath them, they discovered some of Britain's most important ancient human archaeology and proved without doubt that the ancient inhabitants had lived at the same time as extinct animals.

Challenging general religious beliefs, these finds shockingly contradicted long-held views and caused as much controversy as Charles Darwin's work *On the Origin of Species*, published in 1859. After Pengelly gave a talk to the local history society it was recorded in the minutes that local ladies where so shocked by his revelations that they hit him over the head with their umbrellas!

Eighty thousand specimens and artefacts were excavated, providing a unique Palaeolithic history of the ancient human occupation of the Geopark that started around 500,000 years ago.

William Pengelly (1812–94) excavated the caves between 1865 and 1880

William Buckland (1784–1856) encouraged John MacEnery to excavate at Kents Cavern

Small mammal bones were recovered along with larger specimens by the University of Sheffield and the University of Durham during the Darwin Origins Dig, 2009

Hope's Nose, Site of Special Scientific Interest, Torquay

Alan Hart, Collections Leader, Mineralogy Department, Natural History Museum, at Hope's Nose

Raised beach at Hope's Nose, Torquay

Hope's Nose

Hope's Nose provides a spectacular vantage point, but regardless of the view, the headland itself is an exceptional site for its geology and biodiversity, mirrors that found at Berry Head.

Taking the steep footpath to the wave-cut platform, the headland reveals fantastic fossils of delicate corals from the Devonian seas. These were broken by ancient waves and washed in between the large sponge structures called stromatoporoids.

Hidden between layers of limestone are occasional thin dark bands of volcanic ash which would have smothered and potentially killed the reef life. The gentle undulations of the limestone give way to dramatic folds, evidence of the great movements of the earth around 300 million years ago. Perhaps

more remarkable are the site's rare minerals, deposited during the Permian or Triassic by mineral-laden fluids from deep within the Earth. Rare selenium and palladium, along with exceptional, delicate, feather-like crystals of gold, were found. This site has suffered from illegal mineral collecting. However, a recovery project, lead by experts from London's Natural History Museum, has rescued the remaining pods of gold. Using techniques new to science, this project has safeguarded the scientific value of these mineral deposits, ensuring they remain within the public domain.

The raised beach at the southeast corner of the headland is an example of past climate change. Approximately 6 metres above current sea level, embedded with pebbles and fossilised marine shells, this feature is evidence of a period, warmer than today 200,000 years ago.

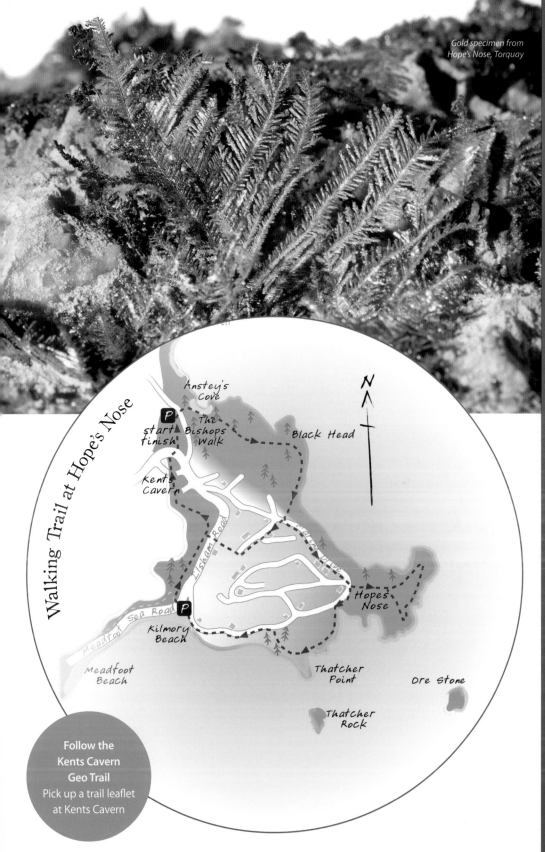

Gold specimen from Hope's Nose, Torquay

Walking Trail at Hope's Nose

Anstey's Cove

P

start finish

The Bishops Walk

Black Head

N

Kent's Cavern

Ilsham Road

Walls Hill

Hopes Nose

Meadfoot Sea Road

Kilmory Beach

Meadfoot Beach

Thatcher Point

Ore Stone

Thatcher Rock

Follow the Kents Cavern Geo Trail
Pick up a trail leaflet at Kents Cavern

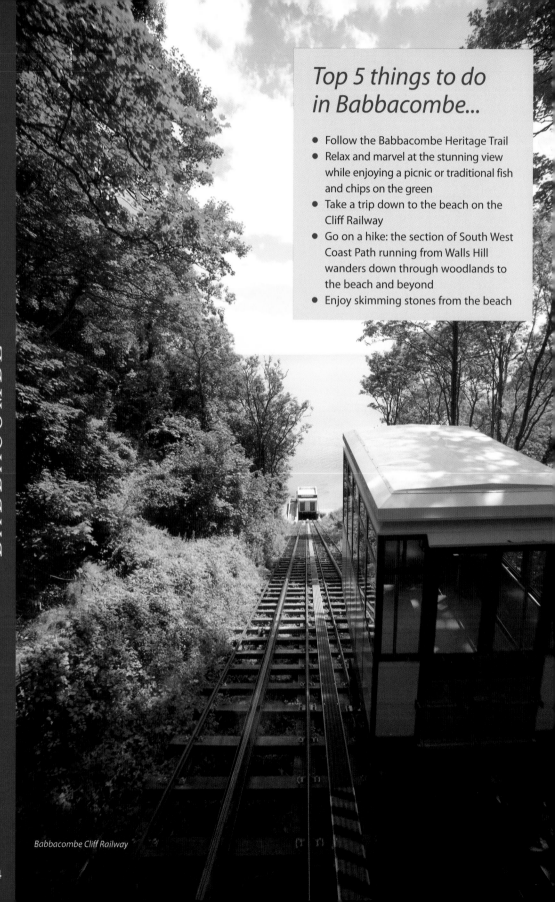

Top 5 things to do in Babbacombe...

- Follow the Babbacombe Heritage Trail
- Relax and marvel at the stunning view while enjoying a picnic or traditional fish and chips on the green
- Take a trip down to the beach on the Cliff Railway
- Go on a hike: the section of South West Coast Path running from Walls Hill wanders down through woodlands to the beach and beyond
- Enjoy skimming stones from the beach

Babbacombe Cliff Railway

Babbacombe

The tranquil setting of Babbacombe Downs offers a view of Lyme Bay that has delighted holidaymakers for generations. The steely grey Devonian limestone contrasts with the red Permian sandstone backdrop, with the vista stretching away towards the Jurassic Coast World Heritage Site.

Below, the rocks have been dramatically twisted and turned by the incredible forces endured during the formation of Pangaea, resulting in the cliffs containing a geological surprise. Layers of sediments are always deposited one on top of the other, with the most recent layers at the very top. The pressure was so great that the older pale limestone, now at the top of the cliff, was pushed over the dark slates, which are actually younger! You can see these slates from the Coast Path between Babbacombe and Oddicombe beaches.

As part of a major fault movement, a massive block of red breccia has moved down between the older Devonian rocks, like a keystone falling from an archway. The historic Babbacombe Cliff Railway, one of the few working funicular railways left in the UK, has utilised the fault line and has been transporting visitors up and down the 73-metre cliff face to Oddicombe beach since 1926.

Above: The Downs, Babbacombe

Above left: Petitor Marble urns

It was just north of Babbacombe that during the Victorian era the existence and value of the Petitor marble were noticed. In reality the marble is limestone capable of taking a good polish; however, it was much in demand and a significant market developed. Its most famous products were beautiful circular tabletops inlaid with a colourful variety of limestone. An example can be seen today in Torquay Museum, along with examples from the town's famous terracotta industry, which exploited deep red clays found within the lower part of the Permian sequence of rocks.

Small blue butterflies on kidney vetch

Greater horseshoe b

Wildlife in the Geopark

The Geopark has an array of important habitats within a relatively small area, from caves to ancient woodland and sandy shore to limestone grassland.

Its unique climate, amazing geology and sheltered aspect makes it a hot spot for wildlife. Many species flourish in the Geopark that are more used to continental temperatures.

Specialist plants live on the thin, dry limestone soils, rare birds find homes on the cliff ledges and farmland fringes, endangered bats roost in the caves and invertebrates such as the Jersey tiger moth provide a splash of colour in gardens and Nature Reserve.

The majority of geology and wildlife sites in the bay are managed by the conservation charity Torbay Coast & Countryside Trust

Vipers bugloss

Cirl bunting, a rare farmland bird breeding in the Geopark

Common spotted orchid

Berry Head ranger monitoring the guillemot colony

Top 5 places to spot wildlife...

- Take a stroll at Berry Head to see the rare limestone grassland plants or stand at the top of the quarry to watch the greater horseshoe bats emerge from their roost at dusk (but remember bats hibernate during the winter months)
- Follow the nature trail at Occombe Farm through ancient woodland and open meadow
- Enjoy open parkland and ramble across the rolling hills of Cockington Valley
- For spectacular views and a range of wildlife follow the bay's 35-kilometre section of the South West Coast Path
- Discover the traditional farmland at Maidencombe, a great place to spot cirl buntings, a nationally rare species

Saltern Cove, Paignton

Snakelock anemone

Marine Life in the Geopark

The marine wildlife of the bay has been described as the jewel in South Devon's crown. Its sheltered mix of sandy shores, rocky coves and rugged limestone cliffs provides a diverse environment that teems with a rich diversity of underwater species inhabiting reefs, seagrass beds and submarine caves. One such site is Saltern Cove, a designated underwater Local Nature Reserve and a geological Site of Special Scientific Interest (SSSI). Seals and dolphins are regular visitors to the bay and basking sharks are occasionally seen.

Dolphins in the Geopark

Top 5 places to spot marine wildlife...

- Take a bucket rock-pooling at Goodrington - the staff at the Seashore Centre will be happy to help you identify your finds
- Look out for seals and dolphins on a Geopark cruise
- The bird hide at Berry Head is an ideal location to watch the guillemot colony, kittiwakes, fulmars and other seabirds
- Go snorkelling at Torre Abbey Sands, Goodrington or Maidencombe beach, where the gentle slope makes them great places for families
- Looking to be more adventurous? Scuba-dive at Breakwater beach to see the seagrass beds or search for beautiful cuttlefish at Babbacombe Bay

Jewel Anemone

Short-snouted seahorse

Guillemot colony

Experience the English Riviera Global Geopark

The Geopark is easily accessible by public transport, with frequent bus and train services operating all year. As an established visitor destination the English Riviera offers a wide range of accommodation and hospitality.

Once here, great ways to see the stunning geology of the bay are to head out to sea on a Geopark Cruise or explore on foot. The South West Coast Path extends from Maidencombe in the north to Sharkham Point in the south, with an interesting mix of easy-access cliff-top promenades, rugged slopes and beachside ambles, that ensure there is something for everyone to enjoy, from the serious rambler to those just wanting a gentle stroll.

There is a network of footpaths in the Geopark, with a range of Illustrated walking guides and leaflets available.

For the more energetic it is possible to choose from a range of activities, including sailing, cycling and kayaking, kite-surfing and scuba-diving.

Geopark activities take place all year, giving people of every age an opportunity to discover more about the heritage and culture of the area.

You can also get a taste for the English Riviera Geopark through sampling some of the local produce and dishes at the countless award-winning restaurants and seafood stalls. The fertile soils of the Geopark provide perfect conditions for agriculture, while out in the bay a world-class fishing industry flourishes, with much of Brixham's catches destined for some of the country's leading restaurants.

For up-to-date information visit one of the Visitor Information Centres throughout the bay or go to **www.englishrivierageopark.org.uk.**

Main picture: Walking and cycling routes offer outstanding views

Top right: Enjoying a Geopark cruise.

Right: Water-skiing off Corbyn's Head, Torquay

Far right: Another successful fishing trip in the bay

Bottom right: The sheltered waters are rich in marine life, making them great for diving

Far bottom right: From sea to plate, freshly caught Brixham fish

Eshaness Coast, Geopark Shetland

North West Highlands Geopark

UK and Irish Geoparks

Alongside the English Riviera Global Geopark there are another eight Global Geoparks in the UK and Ireland for you to discover and explore…

① Geopark Shetland
Walk on an ancient ocean floor, explore an extinct volcano and stroll across shifting sands all in the space of a day. Along the way you will discover some of the most stunning scenery in the UK and find out how geology has influenced every part of life in Shetland.
www.geoparkshetland.org.uk

② Northwest Highlands Geopark
At 3,000 million years old, the far north west of Scotland presents one of the most ancient landscapes in Europe. Here you will find rugged and wonderful scenery, where the rocks tell their history of huge crustal forces, oceans, deserts and grinding ice sheets.
www.northwest-highlands-geopark.org.uk

③ Lochaber Geopark
Lochaber's unique and beautiful landscape is world-renowned for its geology, from its highest mountain, Ben Nevis; deepest loch, Loch Mora; and longest glen, the Great Glen.
www.lochabergeopark.org.uk

④ Marble Arch Caves Geopark
Located in the rugged mountainous uplands and the gentle rolling lowlands of counties Fermanagh and Cavan. Taking in the world-famous Marble Arch Caves, this Geopark boasts some of the finest natural landscapes in Ireland and offers a window into the area's 650 million year past.
www.marblearchcavesgeopark.com

⑤ North Pennines AONB and European Geopark
A stunning landscape of open heather moors and peatlands, attractive dales and hay meadows, tumbling rivers and wonderful woods. As well as being home to some of the country's most special birds, animals and plants, the North Pennines also has outstanding geodiversity, including world-class mineral deposits and a rich mining heritage.
www.northpennines.org.uk

⑥ GeoMon, Anglesey's Geopark
Anglesey has a stunning coastline of Precambrian and Palaeozoic rocks visible along its 125-mile-long coastal path, which provides access to more than 20 varied geosites on the 24 superb beaches around the island. It also has a higher density of archaeological sites in a small area than anywhere else in Britain and its beauty, special culture and language mark it out as a unique place.
www.geomon.org.uk

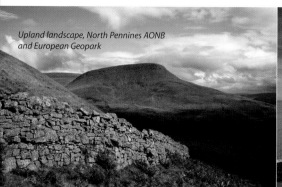
Upland landscape, North Pennines AONB and European Geopark

Penmon Point, GeoMon

Mamore Mountains from Ben Nevis,
Lochaber Geopark

The Porridge Pot, Marble Arch Caves

❼ Fforest Fawr Geopark

From the valley floor to the mountain top and
everything in between, Fforest Fawr, which
translates as 'Great Forest', is a swathe of upland
country included within the Brecon Beacons
National Park.
www.fforestfawrgeopark.org.uk

❽ Copper Coast Geopark

A spectacular coastline consisting of scalloped
beaches and coves buttressed and enclosed
by rocky headlands, the Copper Coast gets
its name from the nineteenth-century copper
mines that lie at its heart.
www.coppercoastgeopark.com

❾ English Riviera Global Geopark

Brecon Beacons, Fforest Fawr Geopark

Bunmahon beach, Copper Coast Geopark

Collecting Code

The geology of the English Riviera is special and vulnerable. Please follow our Collecting Code (www.englishrivierageopark.org.uk) and in particular:

- Please do not hammer or dig at any site without permission
- Please do not remove any fossils, rocks or minerals which are still embedded

Safety Messages

People following the trails and walks do so at their own risk, so when out and about enjoying the Geopark always remember to stay safe:

- If exploring the shoreline always check the tide timetables before you go out
- Wear sensible shoes and be prepared for any weather

- Always tell someone where you are going and how long you expect to be gone
- Keep an eye on the incoming tide as it is easy to get trapped, especially around the headlands
- Beware of large waves in rough weather
- Stay away from the base of cliffs – rock falls can happen at any time
- While walking the coast path keep away from cliff edges
- For their safety, ensure your children and dogs are under control
- Be considerate and follow the Countryside Code
- If visiting by boat or taking to the water during your stay, the English Riviera Harbour Guide will provide you with relevant information and safety advice (www.tor-bay-harbour.co.uk)